D0190443

MICHAEL ROSEN

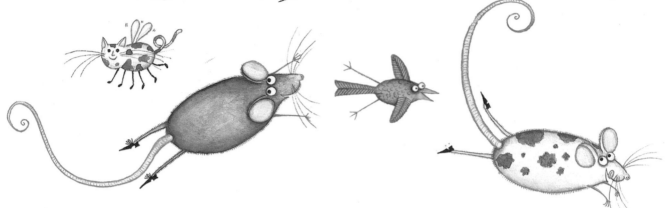

A TREASURE TROVE OF NONSENSE

SHORTLISTED FOR THE KATE GREENAWAY AWARD

MICHAEL ROSEN IS THE NEW CHILDREN'S LAUREATE!

Illustrated by Clare Mackie

A TREASURE TROVE OF NONSENSE

PART 1

FOR 6/455 HOLLOWAY ROAD AND ALL WHO SAILED IN HER

MICHAEL ROSEN

FOR SOLANNE, CAMILLE, FRED, NATASHA, INDIA, ISAMU, FRED, NED, KATIE,
NINA AND LACHIE.

CLARE MACKIE

A Treasure Trove of Nonsense
First published in 2008
by Hodder Children's Books

Michael Rosen's Book of Nonsense first published in 1997
Text copyright © Michael Rosen 1997
Illustrations copyright © Clare Mackie 1997

Hodder Children's Books
338 Euston Road
London NW1 3BH

Hodder Children's Books Australia
Level 17/207 Kent Street
Sydney, NSW 2000

The right of Michael Rosen to be identified as the author and
Clare Mackie as the illustrator of this Work has been asserted by them
in accordance with the Copyright, Designs and Patents Act 1988.

All rights reserved.
A catalogue record of this book is available from the British Library.

ISBN: 978 0 750 04948 1

Printed in China.

Hodder Children's Books is a division
of Hachette Children's Books.
An Hachette Livre UK Company.
www.hachettelivre.co.uk

h
Hodder
Children's
Books

A division of Hachette Children's Books

DIS CONTENTS

INTRODUCTION
TO PART 1

This is not the end of the book. It's the beginning. And while I think of it, this is not a potato, it's a book. Because it's a book it's not full of sandwiches, it's full of words and pictures. This is the end of my introduction.

Michael Rosen.

Aren't you glad it was so interesting and useful?...

Are you wearing jeans?   *No, I'm wearing mine.*

I'm on T.V.

It could be a swimming pool, couldn't it?

SPLISH

When I walk across the room
I hear a splash and a splish.
There's something under the rug.
I think it's a jellyfish.

splash

7

ROSIE ROSIE

......no cake left for us again.

The dog told the cat
the cat told the queen
Rosie Rosie's birthday cake's
stuck in the washing machine.

It sploshed it
it washed it
and Dad had a fit.

Rosie Rosie's whipped it out
and eaten every bit.

......well at least
the cake was clean.

REALLY?

He had a little sticker
and he had a little ticket
and he took the little sticker
and he stuck it to the ticket.

Now he hasn't got a sticker
and he hasn't got a ticket.
He's got a bit of both
which he calls a little sticket.

They won't let
you on the bus
with a sticket.

9

yes!

10

HELP

Help, help
nothing's right
I can't find my ears
and my pants are too tight.

There's a clock in my sock
there's a rose up my nose
there's an egg on my leg
and there's a stink in the sink.

Help, help
I've had enough
I can't find my eyes
and the going's getting tough.

There's bread in my bed
there's flies in my fries
there's a slug in the jug
and there's a ghost on my toast.

Help, help
I'm in a mess.
Have you got my head?
The cat says yes.

The cat says yes,
the donkey says No.
The hamster in the swimming pool
says he doesn't know.

... search me ...

WHEN DINOSAURS FOOLED THE EARTH.

VERY-LOUD-ASAURUS

Seen at big concerts and in school yards.

AREN'T-YOU-GLAD-YOU-SAURUS?

No

SHUT - THE - DAURUS

Have you seen my dinosaur?

FLAT - ON - THE - FLAURUS

I can see you

You can't see me!

Can be used
in the bath as a sponge.

VERY-POROUS

Angel Delight.

HEAVENLY-CHORUS

MY·SIGN·IS·TAURUS

This month look out
for a large dinosaur
who answers to
the name 'Rex'.

GLAD·I'M·NOT·A·WALRUS

I'm glad I'm not a
GLAD·I'M·NOT·A·WALRUS.

ROAD

In the middle of the road it's lonely
the cars go whistling by
I've got no one to talk to
apart from a passing fly.

The noise from the traffic is awful.
My ears are going to burst.
I've been in some terrible places
but I know this is the worst.

I remember being up a chimney
the fire was blazing bright
I remember being in a forest
on a dark and stormy night.

But here the traffic is roaring
I can't describe the stink.
My eyes are weeping buckets
I can hardly hear myself think.

I'm all alone and lonely.
Stuck in the middle of the road.
I'm trying very hard to be brave
I'm a common or garden toad.

WRONG

It's all gone wrong
the singer's lost her song.
She lost the key to her apple
and the bell has lost its bong.

What should she do?
The pickle's in a stew
She lost the switch to her orange
and the shine has lost its shoe.

FRIDGE

There's nothing in the fridge.
There's nothing in the fridge.
Just two frozen peas
and Uncle Joe's sneeze.
There's nothing in the fridge
nothing in the fridge.

NOTE TO CHILDREN

Frozen peas are O.K.

but don't eat sneezes.

DIGGEDY-DO

Diggedy-do
Diggedy-do
The train is late
what shall we do?
Diggedy-do
Diggedy-do
The train is late
what a to-do.
Grandpa coughed
and the wheels fell off.
Diggedy-do
Diggedy-do.

Diggedy-don't!

What's the opposite of Diggedy-do?

BEANS

It's bad out there
it's scary, it's weird
you thought it was hard
but it's worse than you feared.

Next time they say it'll be 'cloudy'
do you know what that really means?
Yes, of course it's going to rain
but it's going to rain baked beans.

Millions and millions of beans
are going to fall out of the sky
all over me and you
I promise you this is no lie.

The streets will be covered with beans;
over houses and cars and vans.
Your hair will be sticky with beans
there'll be beans all over your hands.

Towers will drip with the juice.
Houses will all disappear.
It's going to be something that lasts
for anything up to a year.

Bulldozers will be called into action;
they'll try to move the muck,
but after just a few minutes
most of them will be stuck.

People will go out with hoses;
buckets, jugs and cups
and hundreds of hungry people
will try to gobble it up.

It'll take ten years in all
to clean up every little bean.
So remember – next time you hear the word 'cloudy'
you know what it will mean . . .

FOOTBALLS

There's something I think should be said.
And this is how it ought to be put:
A football shouldn't be round – *or oval*
It should look like it sounds – like a foot.

Should a basketball look like a basket?

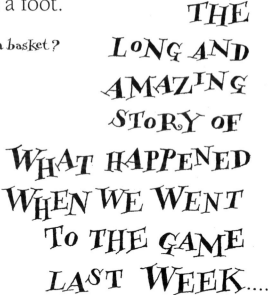

THE
LONG AND
AMAZING
STORY OF
WHAT HAPPENED
WHEN WE WENT
TO THE GAME
LAST WEEK....

I was bored.
They scored.
We roared.

22

IF. . . .

If Dennis plays tennis
and Rocky plays hockey
and Rolf plays golf
and Tess plays chess
and Marty does karate
and Ludo does Judo
and Rose rows . . .

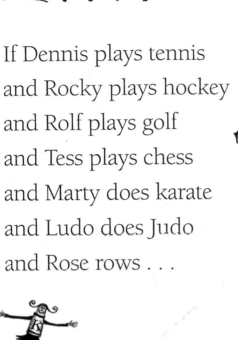

. . . and if Kim can swim
and Dee can ski
and Myrtle can hurdle
and Clint can sprint
and Kate can skate
and Mo can throw
and (like I said)
Rose rows . . .

. . . then who is there round here
who can play football?

. . . and what does Bernard do?

FOOTLING AROUND

A one, two
a one, two, three, four...

. . . footle flop doodle
footle flop doodle.

You can flap your flapper
you can flop your flopper
you can clap your clapper
you can clop your clopper.

Footle flop doodle
footle flop doodle.

You can foot your footle
you can fit your fittle
you can dood your doodle
you can did your diddle.

Footle flop doodle
footle flop doodle.

6 LIMERICKS...

A young man with wobbly eyes
used to muddle his 'g's and his 'y's.
When he said 'guess'
I guess he meant 'yes'
and 'yugs' was how he said 'guys'.

A man with an enormous nose
used to put on fantastic shows.
In his nose he'd squeeze
a swarm of bees,
a cabbage and most of his toes.

This is disgusting and shouldn't be in this book.

• • •

There was a young man with a pimple
who said everything in life is simple.
For weeks and weeks
he sucked in his cheeks
and now his pimple's a dimple.

A boy who told tales called Peter
had news about a huge cheetah.
'What it was doing,'
he said, 'was chewing
a medium-sized thin crust pizza.'

There was an old man from Wales
who was always cutting his nails.
The bits could be found
in a pile on the ground
being eaten by giant snails.

boo!

If he studied a dove he could learn how to coo.

GOOD MOO GUIDE

FROM BOO TO MOO
DR MOO
5 GUYS NAMED MOO
HOW TO SAY MOO

moo-oo!

There was an old man from Crewe
who wanted to know how to moo.
He studied a cow
to try and learn how
but all he could do was boo.

BILLY'S BULLY BOYS

The people upstairs
are making a horrible noise.
We know who it is:
it's Billy's Bully Boys.

They come in late.
They've got hairy legs.
They keep pet slugs,
and put custard on their eggs.

They wear dirty jackets.
They don't bother with shirts.
On Sunday afternoons
they wear yellow skirts.

Mr Billy's Bully Boys
like to spit and cough.
I know what I'd like:
I wish they'd clear off.

❖ T.V ❖ CATS ❖

THE NEWS

Here is The News:
'Two incredible shoes.
Two incredible shoes.
That's The News.

When it rains
they walk down drains.

They glow
in the snow.

They grizzle
in a drizzle.

They sneeze
in a breeze.

They get warm
in a storm.

T.V. CATS

HELP!

THANK YOU

30

They go soggy
when it's foggy.

They've even hissed
in a mist.

But
(sad to say)
there came a terrible frost.
This is what happened:
they got lost.'

That was The News.
Two incredible shoes.
Two incredible shoes.
That was The News.

We're on The News
tonight.

BLEEP

cheep CHEEP

Wait for the bleep
wait for the bleep
bleeps on the phone
bleep bleep bleep.

Wait for the bleep
wait for the bleep
bleeps on machines
bleeps in my sleep.

bleep

Bleep on the freezer
bleep on the monitor
bleep on the crossing lights
bleep on the computer.

Bleep

Bleep

Bleep

Bleep

bleep

BLEEP

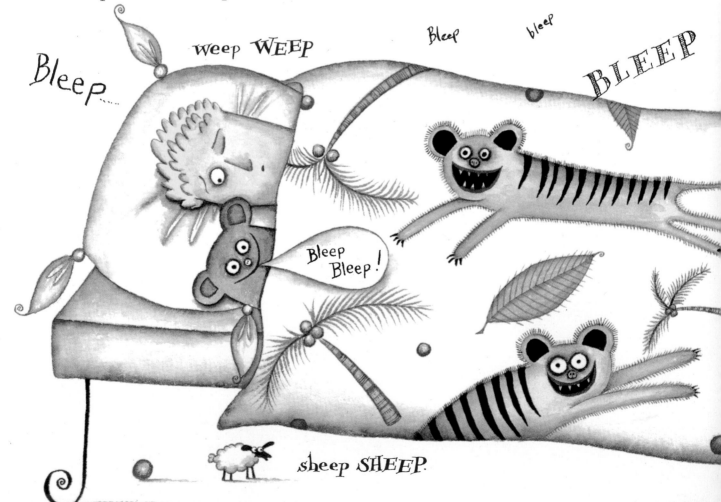

weep WEEP

Bleep....

Bleep
Bleep!

sheep SHEEP.

GET UP

Get up Joe
Get up Eddie
the tea's in the teapot
the sausages are ready.

Get up Eddie
Get up Joe.
Eddie says yes
Joe says no.

So, cover him up with cornflakes,
pour milk on his head,
put sugar in his ears
and leave him in his bed.

THE DOG

Floppy old Poppy
and Whiskers Jim
looked for the dog
and couldn't find him.
He was away
on a trip to the stars,
eating butter
in a house on Mars.

Why doesn't he have
bread with his butter?

34

POLYPROPYLENE

I know someone
called Polly-Wolly-Doodle.

I'm a mat on the floor
just by the door.
I'm tough, I'm mean
I'm polypropylene.

Poly, poly,
poly, prop

prop, prop
propylene

propylene
keeps it clean
poly, poly
propylene.

WELCOME

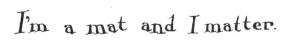
I'm a mat and I matter.

GO TO BED

Go to bed Lizzie,
Go to bed Jane,
It's far too late,
Don't be a pain.

Jane's under the table,
Lizzie's eating peas.
Mum's in the bath,
Dad's going to sneeze.

Go to bed Jane,
Go to bed Lizzie,
Jane's dozing off
but Lizzie's too busy.

DO YOU KNOW WHAT?

Do you know what?
said Tiny Tony,
I've found my foot
and it feels all bony.

Do you know what?
said Auntie Flo,
I think this lump
is a bone in my toe.

Do you know what?
said Mrs Jones
but I think our feet
are full of bones.

Tony, Flo and Mrs Jones
are absolutely right.
There _are_ bones
in our feet.

37

BIPS

Look out,
look out
the Bips are out.

They leer,
they sneer,
they put on nasty grins.
They fight,
they bite,
they lick their sweaty chins.

They mutter,
they splutter,
they show their greasy
fangs.
They grunt,
they hunt,
they go about in gangs.

They yell,
they smell,
they wave their little flags.
And they keep
dead sheep
in dirty little bags.

Look out,
look out
the Bips are out.
Look out,
look out
the Bips are out.

MARY ANNE

Little Mary, Mary Anne
was really quite fantastic.
She wasn't like her friends:
'cos she was made of elastic.

She'd roll herself up
to become very small,
then jump up and down
and bounce like a ball.

She'd tie her leg to the gate
and make her other leg hop,
the elastic would stretch
and take her to the shop.

She could leave a room
and you wouldn't mind
but then you'd discover
she'd left her eyes behind.

What happens if you're made of old sausages?

She might be upstairs
eating jelly;
while you're downstairs
she'd tickle your belly.

She could tie her hand to the table
(this was a wicked trick)
stretch out and let go
and give you a terrible flick.

One day a man came
to measure Mary Anne
from foot to head
and from hand to hand.

With no further ado
the girl was fetched
and with a smile on her face
she stretched and stretched.

She stretched and stretched
this amazing girl
she stretched and stretched
right round the world.

This made her so hot
she began to smoke.
There was a sudden snap
and she suddenly broke.

It was a terrible shame
that it was all so drastic
but that's what happens
if you're made of elastic.

41

MORE, MORE, MORE

supermarket shopping
I can't stop stopping
I can't walk by
I buy, buy, buy
everything on the shelf
I want for myself
everything I see
I want for me, me, me
I'm gonna load up a sack
you can't hold me back

I want more, more, more
more, more, more
more's not enough
give me more stuff
crunch, crunch, crunch
munch, munch, munch

THE BUS

I woke up this morning,
went for a ride on the bus.
A donkey got on
and made a terrible fuss.

She wanted some straw
laid out on her seat.
She wanted some grass
laid under her feet.

The driver said no,
and drove off quick.
The donkey didn't like it
and gave him a kick.

If this donkey tries
to get on your bus
call the police.

TAG-ALONG

Little Johnny Tag-along
wants a pat on the head.
He does as he's told
and gets a kick instead.

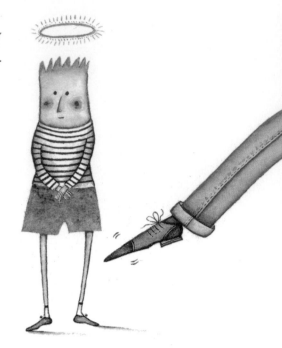

WHO AM I?

My face fell off my head
and landed on the floor,
wriggled about awhile
then galloped out the door.

You ought to face up to this problem.

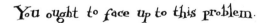

It scared a cat in the yard.
It ate some bread and jam.
It fell into a puddle –
now I don't know who I am.

YUM-YUM

I'm fierce, I'm strong, I'm enormous.
Yum-Yum is my name.
I like to go and watch tennis
and gobble up the game.

I often say to the players:
'Please don't refuse.
There's something I want very much –
I want to eat your shoes.'

I'm not fussy about what I eat.
I want to eat it all.
I start with those delicious rackets
and finish with the ball.

Something I don't understand
but it's nearly always the same.
After I've eaten these things,
they say it's the end of the game.

Game, set and munch to Yum-Yum!

•🐾•T.V.•🐾•CATS•🐾•

46

YESTERDAY

Isn't this the name of a song?

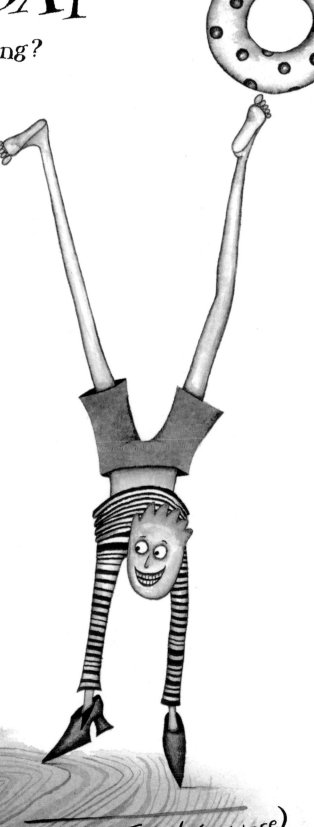

The day before yesterday
I think I'll go to school.
I think I'll take a walk
in the local swimming pool.

The T.V.'s broken
so I think I'll watch The News.
I'll be going out barefoot
in my sister's shoes.

I don't like her,
so I call her my friend.
When I leave
I'll start at the end.

the End (start here)

...and a cat can bat...

POSTSCRIPT

This is not the beginning of the book. It's the end.
Actually it's not quite the end. But that's it for now ...
(for the time being)

not quite THE END

A TREASURE TROVE OF NonSense

PART 2

For Eddie – Michael Rosen

IN HAPPY AND LOVING MEMORY OF
MINTY AND DAVID AND ALDRIC. C.M.

A Treasure Trove of Nonsense
First published in 2008
by Hodder Children's Books

Even More Nonsense first published in 2000
Text copyright © Michael Rosen 2000
Illustrations copyright © Clare Mackie 2000

Hodder Children's Books
338 Euston Road
London NW1 3BH

Hodder Children's Books Australia
Level 17/207 Kent Street
Sydney, NSW 2000

The right of Michael Rosen to be identified as the author and
Clare Mackie as the illustrator of this Work has been asserted by them
in accordance with the Copyright, Designs and Patents Act 1988.

All rights reserved.
A catalogue record of this book is available from the British Library.

ISBN: 978 0 750 04948 1

Printed in China.

Hodder Children's Books is a division
of Hachette Children's Books.
An Hachette Livre UK Company.
www.hachettelivre.co.uk

CAT

THE INVISIBLE CAT

BEE CONTENT(S)

2 BEE   OR   NOT   2 BEE

I remember bee-friending Elsie!

BEE - BOP.

That'll be the bee all and end all!

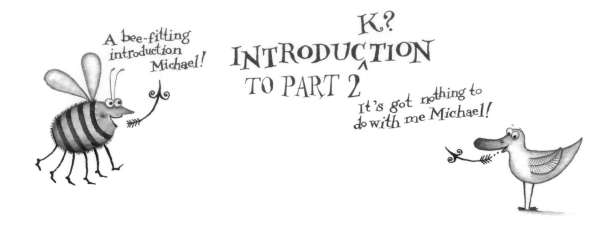

A bee-fitting introduction Michael!

K?
INTRODUCTION
TO PART 2

It's got nothing to do with me Michael!

I think that an introduction is something to do with a duck. I think an introduction is what happens when a duck dives into the water. So far, after looking all round the world and in many, many ponds I have not yet found anyone who agrees that an introduction is what happens when a duck goes into water. So I ask myself, am I completely wrong? Maybe an introduction is something else altogether. I think I will go on another trip round the world to find out what it really is. By the way, this is a book of nonsense. I once did a book that was called a *Book of Nonsense*. This one is called *Even More Nonsense*. I wonder if this means that the nonsense in this new book is more even? That's all for now.

What does he mean more EVEN? It all sounds very ODD to me!

Michael Rosen

It sounds un-bee-lievable to me.......

54

Something That Smells

Something that smells,
we call a scent.
Two things that smell
we call scents.
So something that doesn't smell
we can call a non-scent
and two things that don't smell
we can call non-scents.
If you ask me
this sounds like nonsense.

Do you know why we stink?

It's our instinct.

BEE - GIN HERE

Walking Home

Walking home
in the night,
walking home
in the night
looking into houses
seeing all the lights.

Lights in the windows
lights in the doors
lights up the stairs
lights on all the floors.

But my house is odd.
My house is strange.
The moment I reach home
I can see that it's changed.

There's water in the room
where I go to sleep.
Water water everywhere
water really deep.

There's a man in the kitchen
I see him swimming past.
There's a girl in the lounge.
Oh, she's swimming fast.

There are people upstairs
splashing water at each other.
There's a girl in the window
splashing her little brother.

56

BEE-CAUSE

And swimming round and round
my bedroom wall
is my Uncle Jack
with his old beach ball.

And isn't that my neighbour's daughter?
Yes, that's my neighbour's daughter.
She's come round for a swim
'cos my house is full of water.

My house is not a house.
I feel such a fool.
I used to live here,
but my house is now a pool.

Plonky Wonky Doodah

Plonky Wonky Doodah
chatting online,
Plonky Wonky Doodah
chatting all the time,
Plonky Wonky Doodah
computer nerd.

Plonky Wonky Doodah
'Don't be so rude!'
Plonky Wonky Doodah
'It's time for your food!'
Plonky Wonky Doodah
hasn't even heard.

I'm bored.

P.C. on earth and goodwill to all users!

I ♥ P.C.s

Is that a B-mail for me?

59

My Friend Elsie

THE PERHAPS BEE SOMETIMES KNOWN AS THE MAY-BEE.

My friend Elsie
got very hot.
My friend Elsie
got a big spot.

My friend Elsie
started to drink.
My friend Elsie
started to stink.

My friend Elsie
in the midnight hour.
My friend Elsie
turned into a flower.

Hi, Elsie!

My friend Elsie
went all red.
My friend Elsie
went to bed.

My friend Elsie
smells so sweet.
My friend Elsie
has lost her feet.

My friend Elsie
had to stay in.
My friend Elsie
got very thin.

My friend Elsie
has lost her boots.
My friend Elsie
has grown deep roots.

Has anyone seen Elsie?

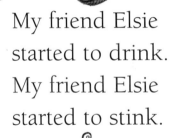

60

The Great Big Hole

Look at the road!
Look at the road!
Right in the middle
is a great big hole.

What shall we do?
What shall we do
when we get close
to the great big hole?

I walk round,
I walk round
right round the edge
of the great big hole.

But you fall in,
you fall in.
You disappear
in the great big hole.

Now there's me!
Now there's me!
Just me on my own
and a great big hole.

61

The Cat Went Out

TAB-BEE

The cat went out on a chilly night
And looked up at the distant stars.
'Why should I live at 23?
I'd rather live on Mars.

I could go wherever I want.
I could become a stray.
I could stay at 49
or walk The Milky Way.'

The telescope she had
from the man at 33
she pointed at the sky
to see what she could see.

'Oh no! Oh yes!' she gasped,
stunned by what was there,
for high in the heavens above
was the gleaming Planet Chair.

62

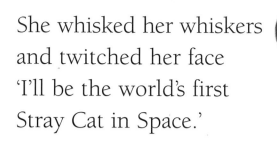

She whisked her whiskers
and twitched her face
'I'll be the world's first
Stray Cat in Space.'

And she did just that.
Her rocket took her there.
She steered it down
and landed on the chair.

So go out tonight,
look up at the stars above
and you might see the cat
sitting on the chair she loves.

Zooming round the earth
at a million miles an hour
was a comfy yellow chair
trailing a golden shower.

She stared at it spinning:
'I want to fly up there
I want to get near enough
to sit on that lovely chair.

I'll put some milk in a flask
and a fish in my pocket
I'll find me a helmet
and take off in a rocket.'

MILKY WAY   SATURN

THE PLOUGH

CHAIR..

Thank You For The GRAPES

VITAMIN B

Thank you for the grapes.
The grapes are great.
Thank you for the grapes.

No matter how many I pick...
The grapes are great.
No matter how many I pick...

I pull a grape off the bunch.
The grapes are great.
I pull a grape off the bunch.

...the bunch stays just the same,
...the bunch stays just the same.

The grapes are great
The grapes are great.

I put the grape in my mouth.
The grapes are great.
I put the grape in my mouth.

I go back to the bunch.
The grapes are great.
I go back to the bunch.

And the bunch is just the same.
The grapes are great.
The bunch is just the same.

I'm a fat cat
who likes
fat grapes.

Grape Expectations

WE'RE HAVING A
GRAPE TIME!

64

You Think You Know

Wannabees

HONEY BEE

MONEY BEE

RUNNY BEE

SUNNY BEE

FUNNY BEE

You think you know
who's who.
You think it's me
but it's you.

You think you know
where we are.
You think it's near
but it's far.

You think you know
when it is.
You think it's mine
but it's his.

You think you know
why I don't.
You think I will
but I won't.

You think you know
what's what.
You think I'm here
But I'm not.

What are you talking about?

65

The Smeenge

'The smeenge, the smeenge
what is the smeenge?'
The parents ask the child.
'It's big, it's small.
It's round, it's square.
It's kind of, sort of wild.'

'The smeenge, the smeenge
what is the smeenge?'
The parents want to know.
'It's loud, it's quiet.
It sits, it runs.
It's kind of, sort of slow.'

'The smeenge, the smeenge
what is the smeenge?'
The parents want an answer.
'It jumps, it leaps.
It growls, it purrs.
It's a kind of, sort of dancer.'

'The smeenge, the smeenge
where is the smeenge?'
The parents are in despair.
'It's up, it's down.
It's there, it's here.
It's kind of, sort of everywhere.'

'The smeenge, the smeenge
what is the smeenge?'
The parents don't know what.
'It's a thing, I think.
A think, I thing.
I've kind of, sort of forgot.'

Hi!

R.I.P.   R.I.P.   R.I.B.

Hi heels.

Little Queenie

Little Queenie, Little Queenie, you know you're a meany
sitting in the middle
of a great big hall.
Little Queenie, Little Queenie, you know you're a meany
hating the way
you're much too small.

You think if you pick on someone very big
someone much
bigger than you,
you think if you pick on someone very big
that you will
get very big too.

You yell and you shout, you boss us about
screaming till your face
goes blue.
You yell and you shout, you boss us about
but we know what
you're trying to do.

Little Queenie, Little Queenie, you know you're a meany
but nothing you do
ever works.
Little Queenie, Little Queenie, you know you're a meany
but nothing you do
ever hurts.

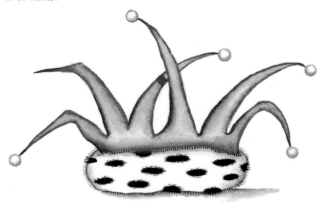

Tony Cross

Tony Cross
Tony Cross
please don't make
Tony cross.

Tony Mann
Tony Mann
it's real cool
Tony, man.

Tony Currie
Tony Currie
did you give
Tony curry?

Tony Reed
Tony Reed
ask the teacher,
'Can Tony read?'

Tony George
Tony George
'George, meet Tony!
Tony, George.'

Tony Watt
Tony Watt
you'll give
Tony what?

Tony Hurd
Tony Hurd
do you know
what Tony heard?

Tony Wilde
Tony Wilde
the naughty cat
made Tony wild.

Riding Down To Boxland

Riding down to boxland
where people live in boxes,
riding down to boxland
the people live in boxes,
no chickens there,
been eaten by the foxes.

Riding down to boxland
saw a box looking good,
riding down to boxland
found a box looking good,
wanted to knock on the box
wondered if I should.

Riding down to boxland
I knocked on the lid,
riding down to boxland
knock, knock on the lid,
though I knocked loud
you'd never know I did.

70

Riding down to boxland
no answer from inside,
riding down to boxland
not a sound from inside,
I picked up the box
to take it for a ride.

Riding back from boxland
the box coming with me,
riding back from boxland
the box coming with me,
laid it out at home,
for everyone to see.

When I got back from boxland
everyone was there.
I was back from boxland
everyone was there,
no one looked inside
there's no one who dared.

IF I COULD GET CHICKEN POX WHAT KIND OF POX WOULD A FOX ON A BOX GET?

FOR YOU

FRAGILE – DO NOT LEAN BIKES HERE

WHY NOT TRY THIS WAY UP TOO

OR THIS WAY UP

COULD BE THIS WAY TOO

PLEASE KNOCK BEFORE LOOKING

THIS WAY UP

73

The Invisible Cat Jokes

Inky Stinky

Inky Stinky Skull Face
doesn't like his Dad.
Inky Stinky Skull Face
thinks his Dad is bad.

Hobbly Bobbly Pimple Chops
looks like Stinky's Dad,
so Inky Stinky Skull Face
thinks Hobbly Bobbly's bad.

MY DAD'S BAD

73

My Drink

My drink started to stink
my dumpling was crumpling.

Dinner disaster
dinner disaster
my head was spinning
faster and faster.

My bread was turning red,
my peas began to sneeze.

Faster and faster
faster and faster
we were heading
for dinner disaster.

My eggs were growing legs
my beans were wearing jeans
my pie winked its eye
my rice was chasing mice.

YuK!

At half past five
my dinner was alive.
At half past eight
so was my plate.
At the end of the day
my dinner ran away.

No more dinner
no more dinner,
this happens every day
and I'm getting thinner.

74

Thinner and thinner
thinner and thinner
my dinner runs away
almost every day.

75

Windscreen Wipers

My windscreen wipers don't want to wipe.
They're old and tired and need a rest.
They've swished and swashed for years and years
they think they've done their best.

So I took them off and brought them home
and gave them each a chair.
They sit and watch old movies,
or simply sit and stare.

They do: 'The Snake Who Cleaned Windows':
the 'Windscreen Vipers' joke.
They talk of scrapes and dangers
like the time the windscreen broke.

They read the papers, have a stretch
and after they have fed
they have a wash, clean their teeth
and settle down in bed.

My windscreen still gets dirty and wet,
it looks smarter than it's been.
Two new wipers, strong and fast
wipe the windscreen clean.

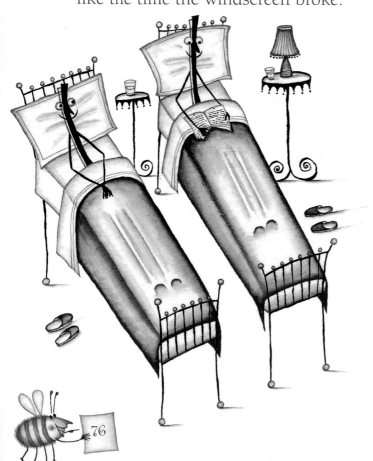

76

Who am I? Why am I here?
What's going on?

To question or not to question
that is the BEE

Our Party

Come to our party!
It's gonna be a crazy thing.
You won't have to dance,
you won't have to sing.

Come to our party!
Please don't make a mess.
Come how you like
no need for fancy dress.

Come to our party!
Don't bring beers.
Please bring your sobs,
please bring your tears.

Come to our party!
Come for a shout.
Come for an hour,
cry your eyes out.

Come to our party!
You'll cry and cry.
We've got plenty of water
so you won't get dry.

Come to our party!
Come for the night
'cos it's time to cry
with all your might.

What's up with them?

Search me..

So glad I wasn't invited

I suspect the weather may change soon in BAR-BEE-DOS...

(SUN BEE-THING N) → BAR-BEE-DOS

Treasure

CAT PILLAR CATERPILLAR

I knew a woman who looked for treasure.
She said she did it just for pleasure.
To me that sounded a little bit funny.
I'm sure she was after a load of money.

One day she was digging an old football pitch –
an odd place to dig if you want to get rich.
Better to dig in castles and forts
but a few feet down she found some shorts.

She realised as the shorts were uncovered
something special had been discovered.
No question about it – this was a stunning find
they were giant shorts for a giant behind.

Straightaway the shorts were shown on TV
all over the world crowds gathered to see
these incredible shorts from underground,
the biggest shorts that have ever been found.

The experts appeared to talk us through:
'Someone wore these shorts, we can't say who.
They may have been rich, maybe poor.
A footballer perhaps. Or a dinosaur.'

Soon there were pictures of the shorts being worn
Explanations of why they were torn.
Giant footballers scoring brilliant goals
Cartoons with arrows pointing to the holes.

Everyone thinks they've got the answer, or nearly,
but no one knows anything about them really.
People keep pretending they are seriously wise
about underground shorts of an incredible size.

And I know this sounds a little bit soppy
but a museum in Florida made a copy.
To show that the shorts were really wide
they say, a whole school climbed inside.

The woman I'm afraid never got rich,
the government closed the football pitch.
There's a book called: 'Shorts in Ancient History,'
but to tell the truth it's all a mystery.

Do mind that hole!

SHORTS IN ANCIENT HISTORY

1

2

BIGGEST SHORTS EVER FOUND – EVER!